Complete Book
of Waiting

A Workbook and Guide for Living
in the Twenty-First Century

JO CARUBIA, PH.D.

Complete Book of Waiting:
A Workbook and Guide for Living
in the Twenty-First Century
Copyright © 2022 Josephine Carubia, Ph.D.

Produced and printed by Stillwater River Publications.
All rights reserved. Written and produced in the United
States of America. This book may not be reproduced or
sold in any form without the expressed, written
permission of the author and publisher.

Visit our website at
www.StillwaterPress.com
for more information.

First Stillwater River Publications Edition

ISBN: 978-1-958217-06-1

1 2 3 4 5 6 7 8 9 10
Written by Josephine Carubia, Ph.D.
Cover design by Lindsay Whelan
Interior book design by Matthew St. Jean
Published by Stillwater River Publications,
Pawtucket, RI, USA.

Publisher's Cataloging-In-Publication Data
(Prepared by The Donohue Group, Inc.)

Names: Carubia, Josephine, author.
Title: Complete book of waiting : a workbook and guide for
living in the twenty-first century / Jo Carubia, Ph.D.
Description: First Stillwater River Publications edition. |
Pawtucket, RI, USA : Stillwater River Publications, [2022]
Identifiers: ISBN 9781958217061
Subjects: LCSH: Waiting (Philosophy) | Time--Psychological
aspects. | Patience.
Classification: LCC B105.W24 C37 2022 | DDC 115--dc23

COMPLETE BOOK
OF WAITING

Contents

Preface #1

"We put thirty spokes together and call it a wheel;
But it is on the space where there is nothing that
   the usefulness of the wheel depends.
We turn clay to make a vessel;
But it is on the space where there is nothing that
   the usefulness of the vessel depends.
We pierce doors and windows to make a house;
And it is on these spaces where there is nothing
   that the usefulness of the house depends.
Therefore, just as we take advantage of what is,
We should recognize the usefulness of what is not."

                                       —*Lao Tzu*

Waiting is the "what is not" of life that may prove to be the most useful in the long run.

If you are committed to boredom, this book may not be for you. If you take initial feelings of boredom as a challenge to activate your inner anti-boredom capabilities, we can be curious together, play together, analyze and synthesize, create and imagine together. We can actually enjoy the "what is not" times of life and the persons we become through these activities.

Preface #2

....

Alternative to turning this page: The "ONE BUTTON" solution.

The contents and impact of this book could be avoided with the ONE BUTTON solution. That is, the button that turns on an electronic device. Don't do it!

Yes, you can find endless distraction, entertainment, and even enrichment on a handy screen, but think about the complex wet-wired electronics and mechanics you have within the magical packaging of your own body! You can do this! Win the game of waiting without external devices!

Conclusion

....

(so you don't have to wait)

Waiting can be fun!

Introduction

There's a proverb attributed to Benjamin Franklin that says, "Nothing is certain but death and taxes." Two centuries plus later, it seems safe to add *WAITING* to that short list of certainties. Waiting may be the only universal and certain experience that doesn't already have a literature, a "bible," or a shelf of "how-to" publications.

Read and work through this book just once and you'll have perpetual, internal systems ready to deploy the next time your flights are delayed, the bus is late, the game runs long, ER is crowded, dinner isn't ready, you can't sleep, you arrive too early, the post office line is long, the package hasn't yet arrived, etc. etc.

Waiting well is elusive and undefined. Many of us avoid even the challenge of waiting by claiming boredom and thus placing the problem squarely on external features of the situation rather than on a combination of unstructured time and a psyche untutored in self-amusement.

I have always taken delays that necessitate waiting to be an intellectual challenge. Isn't my mind capable of endless invention? Don't I have years of experience to draw upon, thousands of books, plays, movies, performances, and family dinners to recollect and replay and revise? Can't I deploy my innate curiosity to amuse me in *any* surroundings? Surely, I won't be defeated by gaps of minutes, or even hours, in entertainment or activity? Haven't I memorized "The Road Not Taken" for just these situations?

I have learned over the years that my own capacity for waiting is not common. Nor is it endless. Most people have a limit between thirty and forty-five seconds before they revert to annoyance and anger or to boredom. I suppose that shouting at a clerk releases tension while eating up seconds of waiting, and it may amuse others who are waiting, but it rarely contributes to a resolution.

There are many strategies for improving our ability to wait, and I am happy to contribute to mitigating the irritation of waiting with this book of brief activities, lists, amusements, reflections, and many other distractions to call attention away from the time that is ticking away between you and your goal.

I don't believe in boredom, and I *do* believe in the ingenuity of the human mind. Waiting is just a test of creativity and imagination, and this book is the guide for getting a grade of "A" whenever and wherever you are presented with this test.

Tools for Waiting

....

1. Eyes

2. Ears

3. Imagination and Curiosity

4. Small notebook

5. Pencil or pen

6. Your copy of *Complete Book of Waiting*

7. Three questions to ask yourself while waiting

Three Questions to Ask Yourself

....

Question #1

What are you doing?

Before you turn the page to see some potential answers, try to answer the simple question, "What are you doing?" Can you get to five?

1. _____

2. _____

3. _____

4. _____

5. _____

"What are you doing?"
Circle any that are true for you.

. . . just taking up space.

Just thinking.

Just writing.

Just listening.

Just looking

 Just nibbling.

Just sipping.

Just waiting.

Just hanging out.

Just between.

Just noticing.

Just scribbling.

Just brainstorming.

Just me.

Just now.

Just casual.

Just drizzling.

Just wondering.

Just imagining.

Just strolling.

Just daydreaming.

Just standing.

Just playing.

Just whispering.

Just pointing.

Just reading.

Just saying.

Just wishing.

Just doodling.

Just browsing.

Just eavesdropping.

Just being.

Just holding on.

Just biding time.

Just peeking.

Just playing.

Just remembering.

Just whistling in the dark.

Just watching.

Question #2 to ask yourself while waiting:

Why did you come? Why are you here?

(Remember, try to REALLY answer the question before you turn the page!)

1. _____

2. _____

3. _____

4. _____

5. _____

Why are you here? Why did you come?
Circle all that are true for you.

To see.	To know.	To make memories.
To feel.	To be stimulated.	To think.
To be touched.	To wonder.	To sense.
To touch.	To be.	To refresh.
To experience.	To test.	To recreate.
To learn.	To interact.	To meet.
To handle.	To go forth.	To intensify.
To marvel.	To be challenged.	To deepen.
To buy.	To try.	To expand.
To converse.	To climb.	To exchange.
To share.	To stroll.	To have stories.
To watch.	To savor.	To build.
To explore.	To renew.	To acquire.
To satisfy.	To be surprised.	To cultivate.
To taste.	To change.	

Question #3 to ask yourself while you are waiting:

What are you seeking?

Try to answer the question for yourself before turning the page!

1. _____

2. _____

3. _____

4. _____

5. _____

What are you seeking?

Circle any that apply for you.

. . . Seeking water.

Seeking color.

Seeking complexity.

Seeking shade.

Seeking speed.

Seeking solitude.

Seeking a breeze.

Seeking diversity.

Seeking company.

Seeking quiet.

Seeking sharp taste.

Seeking motives.

Seeking plenitude.

Seeking simplicity.

Seeking space.

Seeking beauty.

Seeking harmony.

Seeking comfort.

Seeking challenge.

Seeking stimulus.

Seeking balance.

Seeking a question.

Seeking help.

Seeking a view.

Seeking antiquity.

Seeking expanse.

Seeking cozy.

Seeking unique.

Seeking direction.

Seeking perspective.

Seeking mystery.

Seeking authenticity.

Seeking familiar.

Seeking strange.

Seeking the only.

Seeking transcendence.

Seeking epiphany.

Seeking you.

Seeking a sign.

Seeking illumination.

Seeking insight.

Seeking convergence.

Seeking the nexus.

Seeking a word.

Seeking surcease of sorrow.

Seeking a snack.

Seeking a drink.

Seeking advice.

Seeking transportation.

Seeking style.

Seeking a calling.

Seeking faith.

Seeking a deal.

Seeking more.

Simply seeking.

Seeking wonder.

Seeking touch.

Seeking news.

Seeking symmetry.

Seeking solace.

Seeking roots.

Seeking a seeker.

Let's See!

....

No matter where you are while waiting, there are details of delight and wonder. Here is a guide for watching (attending, witnessing, looking, seeing, beholding) while waiting.

Count and/or rate the following:

	(Number or Rating)
People within sight	
Pieces of art	
Communications (posters, instructions, etc.)	
Doors and windows	
Places to hide	
Odd or inexplicable sights	
Straight lines that intersect	
OTHER:	

Observe other animals (humans and others)

Most common clothing item	Item: Number:
% of humans with head attire	
People standing (% or number)	
What are people doing?	
Pet analysis: number, percentage, type, size, behavior	
Potential incidents brewing	
Listen to conversations around you. What are people talking about?	
Choose one person to observe **and** to make up an origin story about.	
What have you learned on line? Not "online," but what have you learned now while waiting on this line here, today?	
What else can you count or analyze in your vicinity?	

Waiting on the Highway:
A Short Story of a Long Wait

We were the lucky ones! We were not IN the automobile accident on Route 80, nor were we IN the automobile accident on Route 81. No, we were in the line of cars stretching for 70 miles in every direction behind the post-holiday, black ice pile-ups in all directions around the intersection of two major highways that December.

Fortunately, we had leftover holiday food and cookies in the car with us. Unfortunately, we didn't have enough gas to leave the car running for the ten hours we were stationary. We ran the car and heat intermittently to keep minimally comfortable, nibbling on leftover stuffing and cookies.

Some folks took short walks in the woods, whether for entertainment or environmental enrichment, it wasn't clear. We emptied a cookie tin and then made good use of it again as a container when we decided it was too cold to walk in the woods.

We napped and analyzed the situation around us, critiquing the behavior of other drivers and passengers, all experiencing the same situation: who was hammering the steering wheel, who rolled the window down to engage in conversations from truck to car, sharing information, who was just sleeping through the excitement. This was BEFORE cellphones! The car radio was the only source of information aside from trucker updates received via their devices.

The ultimate take-away from this situation was that we were safe AND we learned that the longer the wait, the better the story!

Tell (or write) the story of your LONGEST wait. What did you take away from the experience?

The Seven Kinds of Waiting and Why

··

Why is it important to distinguish the different kinds of waiting?

Because these distinctions may have an impact upon your attitude and your attitude is a huge component of your experience of the **quality** of waiting.

1. CONTROL

Description: Do you have control over the conditions of your waiting, or is someone or something else in control? For example, when you are "on hold" waiting for a human to assist you in getting a refund for the flight you booked but can't use. This is waiting of a wholly different quality than being in control of a situation like waiting until after lunch to eat another cookie.

Your recent examples and levels of control:

Example (where, when, what you were waiting for)	Level of YOUR Control (0-5) 0 = no control 5 = you were in control

2. KNOWN/UNKNOWN

Description: When the outcome of your waiting is a reward of some kind (think waiting on line for tickets to your favorite event), somehow the waiting is worth it. But if the outcome is uncertain, or even worse, unpleasant, then the waiting has a different texture, perhaps on a scale from mildly annoying to excruciatingly painful.

Your recent examples:

Example (where, when, what you were waiting for)	Expected outcome (unknown, known, value)

3. FINITE/INFINITE

Description: Waiting for a soulmate would be at the far end of the spectrum from, for example, waiting for Christmas morning. Waiting for inspiration can feel endless, but Christmas comes right on schedule every year! Waiting until your genius is recognized and rewarded? This can slide on the scale, but often tips toward infinite!

Your recent examples:

Example (where, when, what you were waiting for)	Waiting timeline (Infinite? Finite . . . how long?)

4. CONSEQUENCE

Description: Some things we wait for have entirely personal consequences. Others may have far-reaching effects, even global effects. Waiting for your ride after an event is fundamentally different than waiting to attain voting age, drinking age, retirement age, etc. All of these latter examples have societal consequences and impacts.

Your recent examples:

Example (where, when, what you were waiting for)	Consequence (0-10) 0 = trivial 10 = earth-shattering

5. PASSIVE/ACTIVE

Description: Can you do anything about it? Or can you do anything *during* it? Sometimes, no, but more often, I think, yes.

Your recent examples:

Example (where, when, what you were waiting for)	Passive (0) Active (5)

6. SELF/OTHER

Description: Did **you** decide to undertake this waiting condition? Or was it imposed on you externally?

Your recent examples:

Example (where, when, what you were waiting for)	Who initiated this waiting?

7. EXPECTATION

Description: It is easier to wait when you expect the outcome to be positive. If you are on "pins and needles," as they say, it can be excruciating to wait for a response, resolution, or results that are likely to be negative or even more painful.

Your recent examples:

Example (where, when, what you were waiting for)	Expectation (positive to negative on a scale from +10 to -10)

What other kinds of waiting would you add to this list?

BONUS: Transform Your Waiting

What kind of waiting are you experiencing today? Can you TRANSFORM the wait in any way to shift it towards a more comfortable experience? For example, if you are picking up your mother at the airport and her flight is delayed by two hours, can you transform this waiting time by (a) challenging yourself to walk 5 (or more?) miles around the airport, thus earning an extra dessert tonight OR (b) catching up on your sleep in your car or a waiting area OR (c) phoning a friend who might appreciate an unexpected call (not to complain, but to offer support)

Kind of Waiting TODAY	Potential TRANSFORMATION

Your IDEAL "Waiting Room" and GO-Bag

....

If you could stock a special room where waiting would be painless or even enjoyable, what would be in it?

Would it be a small room or a large room?

Windows or not? If you have windows, what would you see outside?

What equipment is in the room; how is it furnished?

Describe or draw your **ideal** waiting room below.

_____

_____

_____

_____

_____

_____

_____

_____

What five items can you pack into a "go-bag" for any time you know in advance that you are going to have to wait somewhere?

1. _____

2. _____

3. _____

4. _____

5. _____

What qualities from your ideal waiting room OR from your "waiting go-bag" would you still have if you are *unexpectedly* sitting in an uncomfortable chair in a train station or a hospital emergency room? In other words, what do you have in your mental waiting room when you have nothing else?

1. _____

2. _____

3. _____

4. _____

5. _____

First, you **never** have nothing! If you had nothing, you wouldn't be conscious of having nothing.

But let's say you have *next to nothing*. That would be a situation when you have no books, no devices, no food, no friends, no gadgets, no trinkets, no distractions. It's just you and your encyclopedic mind, intelligence, and imagination.

What will you access in this mental space while you wait to be rescued or entertained?

1. _____

2. _____

3. _____

4. _____

5. _____

If your previous page is still blank, here are some suggestions:

- Stay away from thoughts related to the waiting situation itself

- Balance on one foot for as long as you can, if possible while singing a song. Repeat with the other foot.

- Take an imaginary trip or plant an imaginary garden, going through each step in the process, slowly, one by one, slowly.

- Inventory what you do have with you, every single, little thing, and imagine what alternate uses might be possible for each item. For example, in a prolonged survival situation, what extraordinary purposes might you invent for each of these items:

Inventory of ordinary items	Extraordinary use or purpose
Sock	
Pencil	
Packet of tissues	
Coins	
Key	

Chameleon Scout Badge: Waiting

To earn this badge, do eight of these activities including the two that have a star.

1. Trade places in the lunch line at school (or work) once a week for a month with someone who arrives late (and is behind you in line) and looks distressed. You can do this while waiting in any line: grocery store, restaurant, fast food, drugstore, etc.

2. Request that your parents pick you up from dance class/ soccer practice/wherever when it's convenient for them, and do not use your cell phone while you wait.

3. Visit the bus or train station closest to your home once a week for a month. On each visit, spend at least thirty minutes keeping a journal of your observations of people waiting.

★ 4. Keep a small notebook with you for one month and log every time you have to wait for anything longer than fifteen seconds. Write the date, time, situation, and how it makes you feel for each waiting incident.

5. Choose a short poem that you like and make a copy of it to carry around with you for a month. Every time you have to wait for something, concentrate on memorizing your poem. Alternate: Memorize your poem in advance and recite it to yourself while you are waiting.
   Suggestions: "Fire and Ice" by Robert Frost
   "Harlem" by Langston Hughes
   "Success is Counted Sweetest" by Emily Dickinson
   "In Time of Daffodils" by ee cummings

Make your holiday or birthday wish list and mark the two items you want most. Consider your feelings and the consequences of waiting to ask for them for one whole year. Write yourself a letter describing why you *can't* wait or why you *can* wait one year for these things you really want.

6. Make a scrapbook of photos and images that show how people wait (or don't wait). Search for and include poems, song lyrics, and sayings about waiting.

7. Interview at least three adults about an experience where something was worth waiting for. Find out what they were waiting for, how long, how it felt, why they wanted it, and why it was worth the wait.

8. Write a story about someone your age who is stuck at an airport for three days because of a huge snow storm. The story would be about what he or she did for the three days they were waiting for the weather and the runways to clear so they could get home.

★ 9. Prepare a list of "Waiting Well" suggestions on a poster or slides. Prepare a list of "Waiting Worsts" (what NOT to do) on another poster or slide. Make a presentation to your scout troop on how to improve their waiting experience.

Accumulating Sight

....

What we see at first is so little compared with what our eyes, brain and mind can accumulate over time. We are like extended-exposure cameras where a photosensitive plate is exposed for a longer period to etch details in sharper and sharper clarity, but only if nothing moves. The aquarium, like the Sistine Chapel ceiling, the night sky, artworks, and faces, rewards the patience of accumulating sight.

AQUARIUM

I realized for the first time today that the stunning rainbow fish in our aquarium can't see me. I looked through the big front plate glass toward the side and could see that a fish was mirrored in all its motions by an exact replica of itself—twins in synchronized swimming motions . . . or a mirrored surface on the inside of the huge tank. The fish can't see our world.

A blue fish with white concentric parenthesis markings caught my attention immediately. At the center of his markings is a bright white circle that any five-year old could draw. In the circle is a bold horizontal dash. Just a short straight line within a circle. What's the big deal? I thought there were no straight lines in nature, that's all. And it looks so designed, not "natural," whatever natural is.

What else is new in the aquarium? There are several coral formations that I don't recall seeing before. One is an unobtrusive peachy tan color with fluorescent lavender tips. The other looks like a lump of radioactive refuse—limey green lumpish rock lit on the surface by bright foils.

Now you try ACCUMULATING SIGHT

Where are you?

At first sight, what do you see?

Keep accumulating sight . . .

Waiting Room #1: Blood Lab

....

"Birthdate?"

"Thank you."

"Address?"

"Thank you."

We are all ages, shapes, sizes, and professions with a single goal this morning . . . to hand in our slips of paper at the desk and to give blood for the purpose of a medical diagnosis.

"I need my lid, here." says a gentleman, reaching over me to get his blue summer cap before going back out to the day's construction work, though it is only 7:45 a.m.

What are those packages some people are delivering?

It looks a little like the solution you drink before a colonoscopy, but they are bringing it IN to the lab, not taking it out. So, it must be some output of the body.

Maybe I don't want to know!

Stages of Waiting: Early

BEFORE it becomes REAL waiting:

Seconds 01-28: Take stock of the situation: scan the area, look over the people on line, examine the clerks or servers, assess the whole system and formulate an opinion on efficiency and customer satisfaction.

Seconds 29-75: Experience and interrogate your first rush of emotion . . . annoyance, relief, anxiety, peacefulness, etc. Can you sustain this? For how long? If not, what progression of emotions do you predict you will experience?

Seconds 76-120: Prepare your items and opening comments for when you arrive at the front of the line. Revise your comments and prepare several alternate remarks depending on which station you are called to.

Seconds 121-130: Look at your watch and synchronize it with any other available clocks or watches, cellphones, etc.

Seconds 131-171: Establish your own, unique waiting attitude and "look" including facial expression, clutch of gestures, and body language (Options: alertness, annoyance, slouch of despair, fighter's stance, zen calm, total boredom, social networker, or resigned despair).

Seconds 172-180: Evaluate any and all amusing possibilities of the place, co-waiters, your own mood, and the potential stretch of time ahead of you.

Seconds 181-190: Depending on amusing possibilities determined in previous step, make a decision of whether to abandon your position or to persist with or without attitude. Utilize additional time if needed.

Second 191: Implement decision.

Second 192: If you are still waiting, recognize that this is now REAL waiting. See Level II.

Gifts of Waiting: "I was waiting, but I didn't know what for..."

After the obstacle course of driving and parking on a scorching day, the shop would be ah-h-h, cool and buzzing with caffeine and books. Workers are painting the doorway today when the extra two minutes delay in the hot sun could knock me right out. OK, be patient and just wait.

Every table looks full as I walk through the labyrinthine small rooms of our one remaining independent used bookstore cafe. Everyone is seeking a respite where the pressure of consumption is relatively minimal—a bagel with homemade hummus, a small creamsicle soda or iced coffee, and occasionally, a book. How does this add up to a business that keeps the door open and pays for heat in winter, AC in summer?

I see only two empty tables in the whole place and settle myself at the elevated rectangular table near the coffee bar. I am just getting the hummus on my bagel and settling to write and have lunch while waiting for a friend when an acquaintance stops by to chat. He is retired now and lives in Arizona in winter. Here in State College, he is doing some community organizing, the passion of his youth. The concept he is organizing is called "Aging in Place," a concierge service for the elderly to enable them to stay in their homes as long as possible. Morey (I only remembered his name when his wife said, "Morey") introduced me to his wife who seemed slightly annoyed that he was so engaged in talking with me. She got her Italian soda and then they moved away from my table. Finally, I have my space back and a few minutes to myself.

A moment later, Alicia, the wife, came rushing back with a big smile . . . "You're (insert name here)!" I said "Yes," wondering why she was so excited now. Turns out she is a friend of May Johnston who took my OLLI course on writing wellness and cognitive vitality. Alicia wanted to take it, but she didn't and now is eager for the next offering. It was nice to have that confirmation that people enjoyed and talked about my sessions.

This was an example of my being annoyed with the interruption of my private space and time and then receiving a gift I didn't know that I was waiting for.

Perhaps we are always waiting for that unexpected pleasant surprise, especially when we wait in public places?

Is there a time when you received a "Gift of Waiting"? If so, write that here.

_____

_____

_____

_____

_____

_____

_____

_____

_____

_____

_____

_____

Stages of Waiting: Actual

REAL waiting: (You will determine the appropriate amount of time for each.)

1. Review your "should have" list, that is, all the things that you could have done differently today that would have prevented your having to wait.

2. If waiting is **no** fault of your own, review a list of those responsible for the situation.

3. Network with co-waiters about waiting.

4. Pull out the magazine or book you always carry for such situations and read.

5. Pull out cell phone and make calls, text friends, or groom your archive.

6. Listen in on other conversations while pretending not to listen.

7. Recite poetry to yourself that teachers in high school made you memorize for just such occasions.

8. Engage other activities in THIS book!

Watching Me, Watching You: Public Waiting Rooms

....

As I approached the ticket line for Amtrak at the Newark Penn Station this morning I smiled at the woman already in the cue. She was neatly packed with a black leather backpack atop her suitcase and a handbag in her other hand. She returned my smile. In some strange recognition between strangers, we acknowledged each other as equals. "Hello . . . Hello . . . In a pinch, you can turn to me." It is unsaid, but acknowledged silently.

The exact same encounter happened to me at the Amtrak counter in Boston's Back Bay station four days ago. Women recognize their peers in age, class, circumstances almost instantly. It's part of a survival instinct when you are alone. Just like instinctively noticing where the exits and restrooms are, women traveling alone identify the peer who will be a potential partner if danger should appear. It's like selecting the person on the sidewalk that you will approach to ask directions.

I was on the train, nearing my own station four days ago when a woman entered the train seeming quite anxious. She asked if a seat next to me was free and we chatted until I got off ten minutes later. She was extremely anxious about this train ride, her very first. "People in Texas don't have this opportunity."

She was so relieved and assured by my very existence as a peer as much as by my words. On both ticket purchasing experiences recently, there was a woman in difficulty at the counter. For the ticket agent, this may have been one of many long narratives that unfold during the day. In Boston, the protagonist was an international person with minimal English trying to buy a complex ticket that might have been impossible. She was short, dark and old—three strikes against her in addition to the language barrier and possibly limited resources. She was holding a zippered coin purse at the counter and I wondered if she would pay for her ticket with small bills or coins.

The agent must have expressed doubt about the feasibility of her desired route, because the customer said, as if in response, "I go this way many time." The agent tried again and then wrote a number on a slip of paper, handed it to the woman, and asked her to wait while she sold tickets to the few of us needing tickets for immanent departures. I saw the price of $148.20 on the paper.

At Newark Penn Station this morning, the woman facing her reality at the ticket window was young, white, and blonde. She had five or six bags at her feet. Not suitcases, but canvas and plastic bags with their handles tied together. She was in an extended conversation with the agent. She told him she had just been released from a rehab hospital, and she needed to get home today. Her voice was urgent and distressed, almost panicked. She rested her cheek against the palm of her hand leaning on the counter and pleaded with him.

He asked for her name and typed it into the computer. Perhaps she had a reservation but no identification and he couldn't give her the ticket without ID. When he asked for a phone number, she quickly gave him a number and told him that her ex-husband was at that number and could give any information needed. The agent ultimately directed her to the police, "around the corner and turn left." She hooked all the bag handles with her fingers and walked off.

When I left the ticket counter, I was relieved to see her in conversation with a policeman. I felt some tug to get involved as her advocate, but I didn't. Perhaps it seemed like a situation that I couldn't fix or even contribute toward solving in the few minutes before my own train left. Because she was connecting with a policeman, I didn't feel entirely as if I had abandoned her to a hopeless situation.

Meanwhile, off to my left is a row of men who may or may not have tickets, but who are sitting along the outside wall of the waiting room on a bench marked (as all the benches are marked) "Seating for ticketed passengers." They are watching, too. They are not watching the big board for their track number to appear. They are not watching the lines at the ticket windows to pick the fastest one. They are watching out for each other as one of them may step outside briefly and then return to the warm station and the benches.

They are also watching the passengers sitting on the other benches. I wonder if they are watching to see if we drop something that they can pick up and use or sell, but when a package of cigarettes falls out of the pocket of a passenger opposite me, one of the watchers gets up and gestures to the man so that he sees his cigarettes and retrieves them. One of the watchers calls out, "Blossom! Blossom!" and I look to see who might respond. I am not quick enough to catch sight of this Blossom passing by.

Leaning against the information booth in the center of the waiting area and looking out over all the benches is a uniformed policeman. He scans the room attentively and constantly. What would happen if he was *not* watching? Is his steady gaze bringing order to this space or bringing safety?

I am reminded of the three young soldiers I saw as I came down the escalator at the Port Authority bus station in NYC on Tuesday morning. They were watching over the streams of commuters.

I wondered if they were in training, sent to this bustling place of transit to observe and learn about people. They were wearing the light camouflage uniforms we have grown accustomed to with wars in dessert and mountain countries, vs the darker green camouflage of a previous generation of wars in jungles. In the universe of humans watching other humans, we may have turned the page from watching to *surveillance*.

Now YOU:
Who do you observe in the waiting spaces of your experience?

_____

_____

_____

_____

_____

_____

_____

_____

_____

Stages of Waiting: "On Beyond Zebra" or "I Can't Believe This Is Happening!"

....

1. Recognize and label accurately your feelings as one or several of the following: anger, frustration, annoyance, boredom, stupor, rage, aggravation, fury, sympathy, curiosity, uncertainty.

   _____

2. Give up. It's over. Nothing good will ever happen again. You might as well just rip up the application, tear out your hair, jump off your chair, drive through the fields, throw all your money in the river, etc. etc.

3. Laugh at ridiculous suggestions in #2.

4. Begin to compose your rant for when you do get through this endless waiting.

5. Become supernaturally calm and pretend to enjoy a zen moment.

6. Actually face the consequences of NOT waiting any longer. Just walking away from the frustrations of waiting. What are those consequences?

   _____

   _____

   _____

7. This time, DO you walk away? **YES NO**

Learning On Line (NOT learning online, but learning while waiting on line)

After the stages of anger and annoyance, you may be able to focus on ways to actually enrich yourself during this hiatus in action. You may learn of a new restaurant from the conversation behind you, or catch up on local news, or merely observe a winning parenting strategy. Stay open to absorbing helpful knowledge or even interesting facts like this fact I learned on line: "The Troll brand bead bracelet will hold Pandora beads, but the Pandora bracelet will *not* hold Troll beads."

"Always eavesdrop and always ask questions!" This was the advice I received one day after I overheard a conversation about a local alpaca farm and then asked where it was and how to arrange a visit. The cash register clerk who witnessed my eavesdrop/question sequence offered her support of this habit when I apologized for breaking into the conversation.

Do you have a story or some useful knowledge gained while waiting? If not, please leave this space open because now that you know of this treasure, you are sure to learn something soon!

_____

_____

_____

People-Watching While Waiting

....

3:16 to 3:26 p.m. Student Union Building, looking out window:

flip flops; 18

jeans: 20

cell phones visible: 13

bikes: 7

Unique (i.e. only one of these): guy pushing a double stroller with two children

Now you do it. Identify categories and count:

_____

_____

_____

_____

_____

_____

_____

Unique vs. Common Waiting Experiences

....

Every experience will have unique features, but will also have some qualities in common with other occasions.)

Try to put something in each box to indicate what might be common features and unique features of the following:

Waiting For	Common Features	UNIQUE Features	Why?
Grocery checkout			
Fabric store cutting table			
"On hold" to speak with someone on phone			
Caffeine			
Your turn to speak			
Waiting for table at restaurant			

Outgoing flight, bus, train, etc.			
Incoming flight, bus, train, etc.			
Dressing room			
To hear about job application			
Loan approval			
College admissions			
Vacation			
Retirement			
Available bathroom			
Christmas			

Birthday			
On line at post office			
On line at bank			
Death			
To live			
To be happy			
To fall asleep			
Tomorrow			

360-Degree Waiting Dance

....

Select movements from this list for each of the body parts/actions below to create your own customized waiting dance. Challenge your waiting companions to execute the dance.

Circular pattern

Rhythmic back and forth on a line

Diagonal tapping

Up and down

High and low

Symmetrical

Asymmetrical

Bilateral symmetry

Shake gently

Waving side to side

To the beat and rhythm of "A Hard Day's Night" by The Beatles

Other: _____

FEET: _____

HEAD: _____

ARMS AND HANDS: _____

EYES: _____

BALANCE: _____

OTHER: _____

Waiting vs. Boredom

....

I don't believe in boredom. Do you?

- ☐ Yes, I believe in boredom.
- ☐ NO, I don't believe in boredom!

I always imagined that even if I were incarcerated in solitary confinement, I could entertain myself with the resources of my own mind. After several lengthy periods of flight delays and waiting, I am no longer so sure.

What is "boredom"? What does it mean when someone says to another person, "I'm bored" or "This is boring!" or even worse, just "Borrrrring!"?

Here is what a few people have said about boredom:

> "Boredom is just the reverse side of fascination:
> both depend on being outside rather than
> inside a situation."
> —*Arthur Schopenhauer*

> "Boredom is the desire for desires."
> —*Leo Tolstoy,* Anna Karenina

> "Boredom is the feeling that
> everything is a waste of time;
> serenity, that nothing is."
> —*Thomas Szasz*

Now I'm finding it fascinating that quite a few people who remark about boredom add an opposite to their statement. Shall we call this "un-boredom"?

What is "un-boredom?"

One more quote:

> "The cure for boredom is curiosity.
> There is no cure for curiosity."
> —Ellen Parr

My Curiosity List:

- I am curious about what my daughter's cat Bella does all day alone in the house.

- I am curious about what people make in "Maker's Spaces."

- I am curious about edible plants in my local wild habitats.

- I am curious about different leads in pencils.

- I am curious about the time-keeping devices and calendars of different cultures.

- I am curious about what the world looks like to someone who is color blind.

Apparently, I can go on for quite a long list! What about you? What are you curious about?

- I am curious about _____

  _____

- I am curious about _____

  _____

- I am curious about _____

  _____

- I am curious about _____

  _____

- I am curious about _____

  _____

- I am curious about _____

  _____

Make Lists: (of anything!)

....

Things I'll Never Do Again (either regretfully OR thankfully)

_____

_____

Things I'll Never Do EVER (either because it's too late OR I wouldn't want to)

_____

_____

Coincidences (good ones, bad ones)

_____

_____

Books

_____

_____

Dares and/or *"I still can't believe I did that!"*

_____

_____

Gifts (for yourself and family/friends for next b'day or holiday)

_____

_____

Favorites

_____

_____

What else?

_____

_____

Spirit Guides

....

Now that you have a little time to think about the important things in life, consider which of these might be your spirit guide.

Crane = balance   Eagle = vision
Dragon = breath   Coyote = cunning, loyalty
Tiger = strength   Deer = sensitivity
Bear = protection   Antelope = action
Butterfly = creativity   Turtle = slow and steady

Other spirit guides that you are attracted to:
(It's ok to guess what the animal represents)

_____ = _____

_____ = _____

_____ = _____

_____ = _____

_____ = _____

Perhaps you are a blend of several? What is your percentage of each of these? And of other animal spirits?

_____

_____

_____

The Wonder of Waiting

I received a phone call delaying my hair appointment by thirty minutes, but I am almost there. Fortunately I have three books with me. I find a just slightly less than impossibly bird-poop-spattered bench where I am just slightly less than comfortable in the slightly overcast weather.

- I WONDER why people leave cigarette butts here on the grass in front of this bench along the river?

- I WONDER if someone planted that flowering tree amid the wild green bushes along the opposite river bank?

- I WONDER if my dangling feet will reach the water if I sit on the edge of that dock and swing my legs down?

- I WONDER what that new structure is at the property over there?

- I WONDER if I can still make it to my yoga class on time if I skip having my hair dried after the delayed haircut?

WONDER is a by-product of paying attention, of noticing the details of your surroundings. Like noticing this small grey bird that doesn't seem alarmed by my presence, but rather seems to be watching me. Watching me wonder:

- I WONDER if that robin knows that the branch above it is a fragment not attached to anything?

- I WONDER what will happen if that robin moves to the fragmented branch?

Wherever you are right now, allow yourself to WONDER and record your WONDERful thoughts here. Notice that many sentences begin with "I wonder . . ." and continue with either "if" or "why." Sometimes they continue with "what would happen if." Try to notice if your sentences have a pattern. Try to write at least one sentence with "if," one with "why," and one with "happen."

I WONDER _____

_____

I WONDER _____

_____

I WONDER _____

_____

I WONDER _____

_____

I WONDER _____

_____

I WONDER _____

_____

Waiting Is . . .

Check all that apply:

☐ Torment ☐ Extra time

☐ Torture ☐ Fortunate

☐ Waste of time ☐ Ubiquitous

☐ Amusing ☐ Suspenseful

☐ Challenging ☐ Boring

☐ A gift ☐ Provisional

☐ Avoidable ☐ Life

☐ Unavoidable ☐ Wasting

☐ Someone's fault ☐ Waking

☐ Inconvenient

Interviews While Waiting

Interview family members, friends, and random people to find out what they do while waiting.

Example:
"When waiting, I look around to find something interesting, and think about that object, only for a moment though, then find something else to think about." (D, age 13)

Your interviews here:

_____

_____

_____

_____

_____

_____

_____

_____

_____

_____

The Endurance Test of Life

Many of our achievements in life require us to do BOTH of these: (1) work hard and (2) wait. We complete our credentials and wait for the certificate. We fill out forms and wait for the accreditation. We take a test and wait for the results. And so on. Make a list here of the achievements in your life and how long you had to wait to enjoy the benefits.

Achievement	Endurance Test Duration

Not Quite Waiting ... Or Is It?

Riding the train is *not exactly* waiting because *something is* happening. The train is a provisional sort of destination. You arrive at the train and then progress toward further anticipated arrivals. It is at once arrival, departure, and intermittent progress (or waiting).

On the train, are you seeing, looking, watching, and attending to all the back yards that appear and disappear as you speed by? Do you imagine the lives of the people who live or work in those places?

When you are waiting at the DMV or at the hospital, do you observe the interactions between staff or the demeanor of solitary workers at their labors?

If you are early for an appointment, is it "waiting"? Are you always early? Or always late? Or always just on time? What does that say about you?

Early? _____

Late? _____

On time? _____

Waiting Formulae: Early? Late? Wait?

....

How to calculate your waiting Adaptability? Capacity? Acumen? Acuity?

E+20=20W+C

Being EARLY by 20 minutes equals waiting plus COMFORT.

L-5=W-5+2A

Being 5 minutes LATE equals negative 5 minutes of waiting time plus Anxiety and Annoyance.

E+10=10W+T

Being EARLY by 20 minutes equals 10 minutes of waiting and Talking to others waiting.

L-20=W-20+50%PANC

Being 20 minutes LATE equals 50% Passive-Aggressive Negative Credit (Half of your credit for attending is subtracted for being 20 minutes late). On the other hand, you have not used any waiting energy whatsoever!

E+30=30W+C+(Ox2)+PC

Being EARLY by 30 minutes equals 30 minutes of Waiting, plus Comfort in knowing you will be on time, plus double Opportunity to have an intriguing experience, plus Positive Credit from organizers of event for your interest.

A15E=15W+6.5NN+RE

Always 15 minutes Early equals 15 minutes of Waiting per episode, plus 6.5 New Neurons generated per episode, plus a Reputation for being Eager/Early.

ACTIVITY: Add your own original formulae for the calculation of "Early? Late? Wait?" using the terms below OR adding your own terms.

A = Always

E = Early

L = Late

W = Waiting

C = Comfort

O = Opportunity

PC = Positive Credit

PANC = Passive-Aggressive
  Negative Credit

T = Talking to others

NN = New neurons generated

RE = Reputation for being
  Eager/Early

_____

_____

_____

_____

_____

_____

_____

_____

_____

_____

Waiting Quotations

Quotable quotes on the topic of waiting come in two flavors: *Patience* is one flavor and *Carpe Diem* is the other.

Patience:
"Good things come to those who wait." And similar quotations. Variously attributed to Violet Fane, Guinness, and Heinz.

Carpe Diem
In other words, "Seize the day!" Or "Don't wait!"

Other:
The watched pot never boils.

Anything worth having is worth waiting for.

"Time is too slow for those who wait, too swift for those who fear, too long for those who grieve, too short for those who rejoice, but for those who love, time is eternity."
—Henry Van Dyke

Do you have any favorite sayings about waiting?

_____

_____

_____

_____

Waiting Room #2:
Toyota "Theme Park"

I do not dread taking my car for its service appointment. I call the service area the "Toyota Theme Park" because it seems to me that a number of attractions are provided to enhance the waiting experience, even though it typically takes less than an hour.

For example:

- Variety of seating accommodations, including high top tables, arm chairs, and massage chairs!
- Beverage options
- Very attractive play area for children
- Art
- Plants
- Free Manicure
- Food Vending Machines
- Restrooms decorated in the style of a well-appointed home
- Lots of visual textures
- Concierge service, i.e. your personal representative comes to tell you when your car service is complete

Here is my informal survey of the **waiting** activities of 17 patrons on a recent visit:

- 7 people on devices, i.e. phone, tablet, laptop
- 4 people reading paper, i.e. books, magazines
- 3 people in conversation
- 1 person staring into space
- 1 person writing
- 1 person doing handwork or a craft

ACTIVITY for you: Take a survey to categorize the activities of others sharing your waiting environment.

_____

_____

_____

_____

_____

_____

_____

_____

_____

_____

_____

_____

Opposites and Actions

....

What does "I can't wait!" mean and what does it look like?

1. "I can't wait to see you!" usually is a positive phrase
   meaning that the speaker is eager to be together with the
   recipient of the phrase. When spoken in an exaggerated
   or ironic tone, it can have the opposite meaning.

Can you think of any other phrases that actually mean the opposite of what the words say?

_____

_____

Actions that speak louder than words: saying "I can't wait!" with actions.

1. Driving around another car to get ahead on an entrance
   ramp.
2. Moving forward out of turn at a 4-way stop sign
3. Cutting in line at the ice cream counter
4. Driving above the speed limit

What other actions say "I can't wait!"?

_____

_____

_____

Waiting Room #3: Flour, the Bakery

- Watching the people waiting
- Watching the people working
- Wondering
- Watching myself wondering:
  - » what if T cut her hair, got a perm, put on weight and I don't recognize her?
  - » What if C gets here first and we don't recognize one another?
  - » Have I changed?
  - » What if T doesn't recognize me?
- Listening to conversations at nearby tables.
- Reading signs and 'signs'

What are you doing in your "Waiting Room"?

_____

_____

_____

_____

_____

_____

_____

Typical Day of Waiting

....

8:30 a.m. Waiting at home
- Do I have time to put clothes in the dryer while I'm waiting? Well, maybe just these very lightweight blouses.
- Not dry yet! I'll finish this when I get home.
- Am I too early? I don't want to be late! I will just go now and read the newspaper.

9:00 a.m. Waiting at physical therapy office:
- Reading the newspaper: "Olivia Newton John has cancer for the 3rd time and will turn 70 this month."

10:00 a.m. Waiting at dentist office:
- I brought two magazines to read, but look at this issue of *Travel and Leisure*! I need a subscription to *Travel and Leisure*!

10:45 a.m. Waiting at the bank.
- This woman needs help getting up the stairs to the bank entrance.
- I have a long list today, but I DO have time to help her.
- "Will you have that in $20s?"
  "No, I'd like two $50's, please."
- She is still here. "Are you going to be ok?"
  "I'm 94 years old and I eat candy every day. I'm great!"

11:15 a.m. Waiting at the restaurant.
- Wondering if they still serve breakfast. Yes! Great!
- Who else is here at this odd time?
  - » Mom, Dad, and pre-school son with very styled hair. Dad sends the boy with a credit card to the cash register to pay the bill. He delivers the items and scoots back to his chair, saying: "I'm just a kid!"

» Another Dad comes in with two youngsters. He proudly announces that his son has completed two days of kindergarten. When he puts the maybe 3-year-old daughter down from his arms, she runs off immediately to explore the space between the tables.

» That's all the entertainment for now. I am the only one in the restaurant, scribbling in my notebook, smiling, enjoying orange marmalade on whole wheat toast for dessert after eggs and homefries.

12:15 p.m. Waiting at the library for a meeting to begin.

· So engaged in the news on the radio that once I secure my precious parking spot, I sit in the car and continue to listen to the piece about women and anger.

· Go inside and watch the crowd wait for the speaker to arrive.

Your typical day of waiting below:

_____

_____

_____

_____

_____

_____

_____

Where? When? Wait!

....

Date: //

Where are you?
Waiting at the doctor's office.

Notes:
- Weather and how people respond
- Spanish speaker on cellphone in waiting area, "*¡Caramba!*" smiles exchanged
- Magazine on the chair between two people: Pick it up? No.
- Prepare my agenda for M.D.

....

Date: //

Where are you?
At home, in bed, waiting to fall asleep.

Notes:
- I slept fine last night, so what's wrong tonight?
- Was it that chocolate I ate after dinner?
- Counting sheep must be a joke, right?
- But I'll try counting backwards from 57 by increments of three.

Date: _____

Where are you? _____

Try this:

_____

_____

_____

Notes:

_____

_____

_____

_____

_____

_____

_____

_____

Date: / /

Where are you?
On campus, waiting for a colleague to arrive for my assistance.

Notes:
- So glad to have found parking and easy access and seating in our meeting place.
- Time to consider WHY I offer my time and expertise to assist a younger person in her career.
- Campus is a great place for reading tee shirts, backpacks, ripped jeans, hair styles, confidence, backgrounds, etc. A huge lecture class just got out and fabulous diversity is streaming right past me!

Date: _____

Where are you? _____

Try this:

_____

_____

_____

Notes:

_____

_____

_____

_____

_____

_____

_____

_____

Date: / /

Where are you?
Waiting for class outside locked classroom.

Notes:
- I overheard a young woman say this to her boyfriend (I assume): "Sorry I asked!"
- Makes me think: Why do we say "sorry" when we don't mean it? Do I do that, too?

Date: _____

Where are you? _____

Try this:

_____

_____

_____

Notes:

_____

_____

_____

_____

_____

_____

_____

_____

Date: / /

Where are you?
Anywhere; waiting for the pain to end.

Notes:
- Pain just takes over my mind.
- Is it true that if you are reciting poetry that you have memorized, your brain has no room for pain?
- Pain changes me into someone else? Who?
- But it's not even that bad. What about people who have chronic severe pain?
- What am I NOT doing because of the pain?

· ·

Date: / /

Where are you?
Waiting for the Thai food I ordered to be ready.

Notes:
- Eat a snack from my purse.
- Wonder, "What would happen if I climbed up on that wooden horse in the center of the room?"
- Walk around outside the restaurant.
- Notice haircuts: Is that a Mohawk ? Oh, let's change the name of that haircut! What should it be called? Coal miner haircut? Penguin haircut? The Blade?

Date: _____

Where are you? _____

Try This: (use one or two of these for each blank page)
- Memorize a short poem (always carry a poem you intend to memorize)
- Inventory the space for engaging features
- Consider what you have been meaning to figure out: your shopping list, your next assignment at school or work, what you want for your birthday, etc.
- Select a person or group to observe more closely
- Imagine what you could be doing if you weren't waiting
- Check out the "Better; NOT" page in this book

Notes:

_____

_____

_____

_____

_____

_____

_____

Better or Not

....

Waiting is better than <u>falling</u>, but NOT as good as <u>flying</u>.
Waiting is better than <u>explaining</u>, but NOT as good as <u>eating</u>.
Waiting is better than <u>paying</u>, but NOT as good as <u>swimming</u>.

Now you:

Waiting is better than _____ ,

but NOT as good as _____ . .

Waiting is better than _____ ,

but NOT as good as _____ . .

Waiting is better than _____ ,

but NOT as good as _____ . .

Waiting is better than _____ ,

but NOT as good as _____ . .

Waiting is better than _____ ,

but NOT as good as _____ . .

Counting on Waiting

Things to count while you are waiting:

- People passing by on cellphones

- Men and boys arranging their private parts

- Women touching their hair

- People chewing gum

- People wearing hats

- % of children vs. adults

- % of men vs. women

- # of people wearing specific colors, how many wearing red, purple, grey, etc.

- Live plants in an indoor space

- Outdoors: count trucks vs. cars vs. motorcycles vs. bicycles

- People alone vs. groups

- What else?

Waiting While Going Out of My Mind!

Number the following responses in the order you will use them:

_____   Blame someone (not myself) for this delay!

_____   Take deep breaths and clear my mind.

_____   Pinch myself to wake up from this nightmare!

_____   Promise myself a reward for not screaming.

_____   Regret (vividly) the other options you didn't take today.

_____   Complain (loudly) to the person next to you.

_____   Give yourself an immediate reward (NOW!) for **not** stabbing anyone with your pencil.

_____   Balance on one foot while karate-kicking with the other. Repeat.

Other activities you are contemplating while waiting:

_____

_____

_____

_____

Waiting Room #4: Gate 11 at PVD

I am/we are waiting at PVD airport, Gate 11 for the 6:15 a.m. flight to ORD.

You are getting your shoes shined and I go to buy water and get a seat at our boarding gate. I am facing the direction you will come from so I can spot you walking towards me.

I am waiting for you.

I am waiting for you.

I am waiting for you.

I am waiting for you.

I find a reason to expect you, to need you **now**—I will say that I need to go to the bathroom.

This waiting so hard is not working! I can't know how many news and sports bulletins you and Shoeshine Man will discuss while I am waiting.

I think I see you once, twice, again.

I decide to STOP waiting.

STOP. Just STOP waiting.

I flip the switch from waiting for you to watching, noticing the faces, seeing them, each individual inhabited by one individual, not by the absence of you.

Breathe easy.

Notice, don't wait.

Is it that simple? I feel my shoulders loosen up. I feel lighter, looser, lifted.

Ah, that's better!

I'm <u>not</u> waiting.

I'm just here.

And so are you.

Famous Waiting, i.e. Writing While Waiting or Waiting While Writing

···

(And summaries so you don't have to wait to decide if you want to find this and read it for yourself and/or pack it in your "Waiting GO-Bag".)

Waiting for Godot by Samuel Beckett (drama first performed in 1953)

This play is considered a tragicomedy with both tragic and comedic elements. Essentially, two men wait for a third man to arrive. He never arrives. Recommended for those with a quirky sense of humor.

"I Am Waiting" by Lawrence Ferlinghetti (poem published in 1958 book, *A Coney Island of the Mind*)

The poem is a list of ambitious aspirations for the USA. The most magnificent line, repeated in the poem, is, "I am perpetually awaiting a rebirth of wonder."

"Waiting—A Field at Dusk" poem by Robert Frost (1874-1963)

The poet is alone in a field dreaming/waiting for someone who is not there.

Waiting to Exhale (1995 movie based on 1992 book of the same name by Terry McMillan)

Romantic comedy in which four women share life experiences as they consider making commitments to romantic relationships.

Wait Wait...Don't Tell Me! (humorous news quiz show on NPR radio)

"Good things come to those who wait."
Advertising campaign slogan for Heinz catsup and for Guinness stout.

What other books, movies, poems, songs are about waiting?

1. _____

2. _____

3. _____

4. _____

5. _____

If **you** were to write about waiting, what would you write?

_____

_____

_____

_____

_____

_____

_____

Book of Waiting: Categories Game

Instructions and Hints:

Complete the grid on page 89 by using words/numbers from the list below.

Hints:

- Underlined words may be headings of columns.
- Words in **bold** may be **Types of Waiting** (first column?)
- Some words may be used more than once.
- There may be extra words, not used at all.
- Every position on the grid should be filled
- After completing the Categories Grid, read each row across, from left to right, for maximum relief. For extra points, create additional categories, columns, and word/number lists.

Word/Number List:

floating	office	**Healing/Therapeutic**
laugh	81	67
monthly	scream	**Amusing**
grey	car	12
Location	**Somber**	Percent
daily	weekly	imagine
itchy	run!	Aura
sleep	light	underwear
Annoying	Options	bi-weekly

	Types	Results
mall	faint	bed
pimples	endure	yellow/green stripes
cloudy	**Everyday**	dots and dashes
rarely	yearly	underwater
2	wet	escape
Spectacular	static	**Routine**
headache	faint	amusing
cranky	park	24
floating	giggles	Frequency
"roof"	33	100
16		

Book of Waiting: Categories Game

About the Author

Jo Carubia, Ph.D. began her career as an educator teaching English and Spanish in a middle school. As she shifted careers and eventually began teaching lawyers how to maximize their use of computerized data and documents, she realized that **no one** could surprise her in the classroom. Middle school students had taught her all their tricks! That early-teen, energized spirit of zany humor and vitality animates this book. If you believe, as the author believes, that there *is no such thing as boredom*, come along and seize the moment! It's better than zen; better than your mother's advice to "Be patient!" As a young teen, Carubia wrote a poem deploring the concept of "Delayed Gratification" that required her to wait endlessly for her goals to be realized. Now, she has created a guide to transform the nuisance and agony of delays into delights!

In addition to middle school and law firms in New York City, Dallas, and Washington, DC, Jo Carubia, Ph.D. has experience teaching high school, community college, at Penn State University, and in community settings. She worked in publishing in NYC and Stamford CT, and served as Chief Academic Liaison Officer for the Penn State Milton S. Hershey Medical Center and College of Medicine. As a lifelong early arriver, she also has ample experience waiting.

Made in United States
North Haven, CT
11 June 2022

20126094R00065